What Else Can I
Flute
Grade One

Series Editor: Mark Mumford

Music arranged and processed by
Barnes Music Engraving Ltd
East Sussex TN22 4HA, England

Published 1995

Introduction

In this *What Else Can I Play?* collection you'll find sixteen popular tunes that are both challenging and entertaining.

The pieces have been carefully selected and arranged to create ideal supplementary material for young flautists who are either working towards or have recently taken a Grade One flute examination.

Technical demands increase progressively, gradually introducing new concepts that reflect the requirements of the major examination boards. Each piece offers suggestions and guidelines on breathing, dynamics and tempo, together with technical tips and performance notes.

Pupils will experience a wide variety of music, ranging from folk and classical through to showtunes and popular songs, leading to a greater awareness of musical styles.

Whether it's for light relief from examination preparation, or to reinforce the understanding of new concepts, this collection will enthuse and encourage all young flute players.

Note: references to fingering within this book use Thumb 1 2 3 4.

What Else Can I Play?
Flute
Grade One

Little donkey

Words and Music by Eric Boswell

This nativity song, with its simple melody, has continued to be a favourite since its composition in 1959.

This tune is best played with a smooth-flowing *cantabile* or 'singing' style. Remember to play F sharps, as in the key signature and don't forget to keep your left hand first finger off when playing D.

2

The blue bell of Scotland

Traditional

This song is said to date from around the year 1800. It is commonly misnamed 'The Blue Bells of Scotland'. The words describe the fears suffered by those whose loved ones are away at war.

You may need to breathe in the middle of each four bar phrase but always try to look toward the end of the phrase, to give the whole piece a feeling of continuity. Play with a nice strong sound at the end when the original tune is restated, being careful not to overblow.

The ash grove

Traditional

'The Ash Grove' is a traditional Welsh folk song, also known as 'Llwyn On'.

Keep an even tempo and try giving just a little emphasis to the first beat of each bar. When you play the repeat remember to go straight to the second time bar.

May each day

Words by Mort Green, Music by George Wyle

This song was a hit for Andy Williams in 1966. Andy Williams is one of America's most popular singers and has recorded over fifty albums.

This piece is in the key of G major so watch out for F sharps but also notice there are some F naturals in bars 9 and 10. Playing *crescendo* and *diminuendo*, where marked, will help make the music expressive and more interesting. Remember to only tongue the first of the tied notes!

Edelweiss

Words by Oscar Hammerstein II, Music by Richard Rodgers

The edelweiss is the national flower of Switzerland. The song 'Edelweiss' is sung by Maria in the celebrated musical *The Sound Of Music*. The writing partnership of Rodgers and Hammerstein was responsible for some of the most famous musicals ever staged, including *South Pacific*, *The King And I*, *Carousel* and *Oklahoma!*

Play this melody as you would imagine it being sung. Use soft tonguing and make sure that you always aim for the end of the phrases. Watch out for the crescendo and diminuendo in the middle section – but don't overdo it!

Cavatina

Music by Stanley Myers

'Cavatina' is the theme tune from the 1978 film *The Deer Hunter*. The most famous version was recorded by guitarist John Williams, but it was also performed as a song 'He Was Beautiful', with words by Cleo Lane.

This piece needs to be played with feeling, whilst keeping the tempo steady. Don't tongue the notes too hard – try tonguing 'd' instead of 't'. To help you make a full, round sound be sure that your shoulders and neck are relaxed – especially at bar 21.

Rigadoon

Henry Purcell

Allegretto (♩ = 112)

When he was just fifteen, Henry Purcell (1659-1695) was employed to tune the organ in Westminster Abbey. At the age of eighteen he was commissioned to compose music for the King. His works include the first (some say only) great English opera, *Dido And Aeneas*.

There's some tricky articulation (tonguing and slurring) in this piece. Don't over shorten the *staccato* notes. Use your diaphragm to push through the slurred notes in bars 11 and 15.

Hushabye mountain

Words and Music by Richard M Sherman and Robert B Sherman

Moderato (♩ = 92)

The Sherman brothers, the writers of this song, enjoyed a fruitful association with Walt Disney. They provided the scores to several classic films, among them *Mary Poppins* (1964), *The Jungle Book* (1967) and *Chitty Chitty Bang Bang* (1968).

Don't take this tune too slowly and do remember the crescendo and diminuendos. Try to create a *doloroso* (sorrowful) mood – thinking of something sad might help! Watch your left hand position, particularly for the G sharps in the second to last bar. You should always keep your fingers close to the keys. Use a mirror to check.

Lullaby

Johannes Brahms

Johannes Brahms (1833-1897) was a German pianist and composer who was greatly influenced by German folk music and Hungarian violin music. Some of his earliest playing engagements were in dockside taverns.

A lullaby is a cradle song. Imagine that you really are trying to sing a baby to sleep. The dynamics are *piano* (soft) and *mezzo piano* (medium soft). Be careful with the octave jumps in bars 10-11 and 14-15. Make sure the high G doesn't leap out abruptly and wake the baby!

I whistle a happy tune

Words by Oscar Hammerstein II, Music by Richard Rodgers

This song is from the musical *The King And I*. It is sung by the character Anna as she arrives to take up her post as Governess to the children of the King of Siam. Other famous songs from the show include 'Getting To Know You' and 'Shall We Dance'.

A cheerful performance is called for (the middle section of the tune is actually whistled in the original version). Keep the staccato notes light and remember to add the accents where they appear. Don't panic when you meet the A sharps in bars 10 and 20 – they're just like B flats but under another name.

Love theme from the Thorn Birds

Henry Mancini

Composer Henry Mancini wrote film scores for *Breakfast At Tiffany's* and *The Pink Panther* as well as this music for the epic TV serialisation of Colleen McCullough's *The Thorn Birds*. When the series was shown in Britain it so captivated its audience that, after the final episode, the National Grid struggled to cope with one of its biggest ever power drains as millions of viewers switched on their kettles.

In the opening bars of this tune the crotchet rests, on beat one, are quite important, so count it through carefully. Remember, this is a love theme and should be *molto legato* (very smooth) and expressive. To avoid making 'in between' notes (for example in bars 6 and 8) check your fingers all move at the same time when changing notes.

Sing a rainbow

Words and Music by Arthur Hamilton

There seems to be very little known about the writer of this song, Arthur Hamilton. The song is about the different colours that appear together in a rainbow.

Practise the quavers in bars 5, 8 and 9 slowly at first so that the notes are clear and even. You can push your breath faster to reach higher notes at the end of phrases, but take care not to overblow. Imagine you are huffing, as if to make mist on the surface of a mirror, and remember to direct the airstream across – not down into the flute.

Love is like a butterfly

Words and Music by Dolly Parton

This song was used as the theme tune for Carla Lane's TV sitcom *Butterflies*. It was originally a hit for country singer Dolly Parton.

The syncopated rhythm in bar 4 might seem easier if you think of it as ♫♩. You could decide to use your Thumb B flat key in bar 9 but then do remember to change back before the next phrase. Observing the diminuendo should also help you to conserve breath.

If

Words and Music by David Gates

This romantic ballad, written by David Gates of the pop group Bread, was a hit for them in 1971.

Be aware of your left hand position when playing A flat and G sharp. Your third and little fingers should be curved rather than straight, although this may be difficult if you have small hands.

Eye level

Jack Trombey

Allegretto (♩ = 112)

This tune, by composer Jack Trombey, is most famous in the version recorded by the Simon Park Orchestra as the theme for a TV series called *Van Der Valk*.

Rhythmically the piece is quite challenging, but because of all the syncopation it's also great fun. The long notes aren't as bad as they look since the tempo is quite brisk, but do make good use of the breath marks. In bar 22 you may find it easier to use your Thumb B flat key.

Tie me kangaroo down, sport

Words and Music by Rolf Harris

Moderato (♩ = 120)

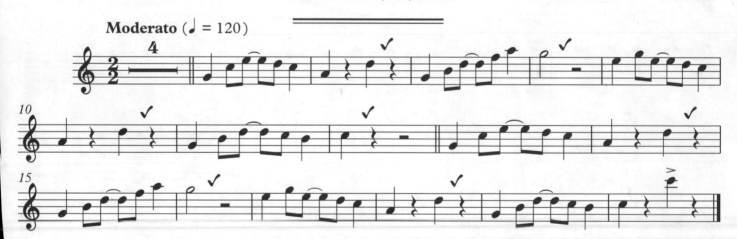

Australian artist Rolf Harris found fame with this song in 1960. His later hits include 'Sun Arise', 'Two Little Boys' and, quite unexpectedly in 1993, his own slightly tongue-in-cheek version of Led Zeppelin's 'Stairway To Heaven'.

This piece should be fun to play. It's lively and humorous, a little bit like a calypso. First check your rhythms, slowly. When you know the tune well enough, experiment with the rhythm by feeling the count as two in a bar.

Little donkey

Words and Music by Eric Boswell

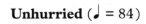

4

The blue bell of Scotland

Traditional

The ash grove

Traditional

Allegretto (♩ = 100)

May each day

Words by Mort Green, Music by George Wyle

Edelweiss

Words by Oscar Hammerstein II, Music by Richard Rodgers

Cavatina

Music by Stanley Myers

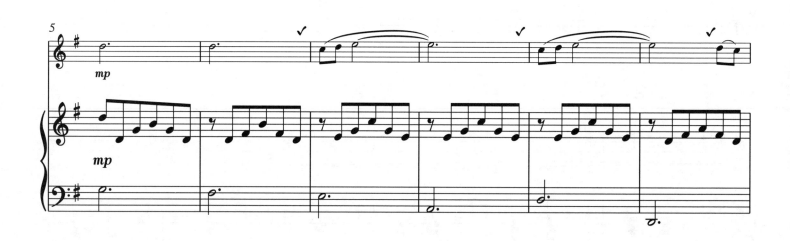

Rigadoon

Henry Purcell

Hushabye mountain

Words and Music by Richard M Sherman and Robert B Sherman

rit.

Lullaby

Johannes Brahms

I whistle a happy tune

Words by Oscar Hammerstein II, Music by Richard Rodgers

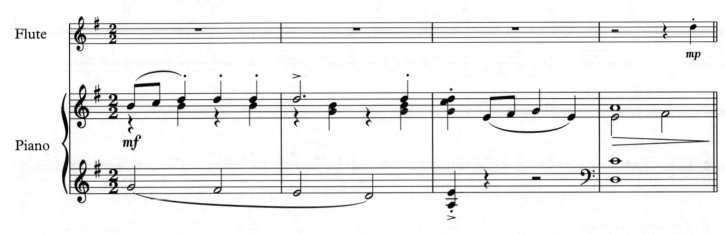

Love theme from the Thorn Birds

Henry Mancini

Sing a rainbow

Words and Music by Arthur Hamilton

Love is like a butterfly

Words and Music by Dolly Parton

Moderato (♩ = 100)

If

Words and Music by David Gates

Steady 4 (♩ = 92)

Eye level

Jack Trombey

Tie me kangaroo down, sport

Words and Music by Rolf Harris

Reproduced and printed by
Halstan & Co. Ltd., Amersham, Bucks., England